COMPREHENSION NINJA WORKBOOK

AGES 10–11

ANDREW JENNINGS

BLOOMSBURY EDUCATION
LONDON OXFORD NEW YORK NEW DELHI SYDNEY

BLOOMSBURY EDUCATION
Bloomsbury Publishing Plc
50 Bedford Square, London, WC1B 3DP, UK
29 Earlsfort Terrace, Dublin 2, Ireland

BLOOMSBURY, BLOOMSBURY EDUCATION and the Diana logo are trademarks of
Bloomsbury Publishing Plc

First published in Great Britain, 2020 by Bloomsbury Publishing Plc
Text copyright © Andrew Jennings, 2020

Ninja illustrations copyright © Andrew Jennings, 2020
Illustrations copyright © David Hurtado, 2020

Andrew Jennings has asserted his right under the Copyright, Designs and Patents Act, 1988,
to be identified as Author of this work

A catalogue record for this book is available from the British Library

ISBN: PB: 978-1-4729-8514-9; ePDF: 978-1-4729-8515-6

4 6 8 10 9 7 5 3

Text design by Marcus Duck Design

Printed and bound in the UK by Ashford Colour Press

To find out more about our authors and books visit www.bloomsbury.com and sign up for
our newsletters

Acknowledgements

To Christopher Hole, thank you for the inexhaustible level of quality you have brought to the
Comprehension Ninja series and beyond. Your subject knowledge, skills and experience have
been essential in developing the highest quality non-fiction texts, that are engaging, inspiring
and informative for the reader.

INTRODUCTION

Reading comprehension is all about understanding what you are reading – and being able to show that you understand. This Comprehension Ninja workbook will help your child master the foundations of reading comprehension by focusing on three key aspects:

- **Skimming** and **scanning** a whole text to locate information efficiently.
- **Retrieving** the correct information from the text in eight different ways.
- **Vocabulary** awareness and the **effect of word choices.**

This book contains seven curriculum-linked texts, each followed by a set of questions to check whether your child has understood the text. There are eight question types to develop your child's comprehension skills:

 Labelling   Matching    Fill in the gap    Multiple choice

 True or false   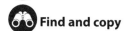 Find and copy    Sequencing    Underline or highlight

For texts 1 - 4, the activity pages feature one question type per page so your child can focus on building up their comprehension skills one at a time, while texts 5 - 7 look a bit more like a test, with two pages of mixed questions.
This book includes the following topics: the Battle of Hastings, Barack Obama, dinosaurs, climate change, Ancient Mayan civilisation, plants and gaming consoles.

HOW TO USE THIS WORKBOOK

STEP 1 – READ THE TEXT CAREFULLY

Encourage your child to read the whole text carefully before they start trying to answer the questions. You can help them with any words or phrases they don't know. As an extra activity, you could ask your child to read the text aloud to you.

STEP 2 – PICK OUT KEY WORDS AND INFORMATION

Picking out key words and headings will help your child to quickly locate the information they need to answer the questions. Encourage your child to underline key information as they read the text, such as:

- **Nouns** – names of people, places and objects.
- **Time** – dates and periods of time.
- **Numbers** – amounts, statistics, percentages and figures.
- **Vocabulary** – important topic vocabulary or words they are unsure of. They could look these up online or in a dictionary to find out what they mean.

Your child should also look out for titles and headings, which will help them understand the structure of the text.

STEP 3 – IDENTIFY KEY WORDS IN THE QUESTIONS

Encourage your child to identify key words in the questions so they know what they're looking for to find the answer. For example, in a text about the seaside:

> **Question**: What might you find in a rock pool?
>
> **Key words**: rock pool

'Rock pool' is the clue needed to answer the question.

STEP 4 – SKIM AND SCAN THE TEXT

Once your child has identified the key words in the question, they can try to remember where in the text the answer can be found. This might be as simple as remembering whether it was at the beginning, middle or end of the text, or thinking about which section the key information was in.

Your child can then **skim read** the whole text to find the section they need. When they've found it, they should **scan** the section to find the relevant sentences. They then read those sentences carefully to find the answer.

Invite your child to work through all the questions and give them lots of encouragement along the way. The answers can be found at the back of the book.

1 THE BATTLE OF HASTINGS

The Battle of Hastings is one of the most famous and bloody battles in British history. On the morning of 14 October 1066, two armies prepared to fight for the throne of England. Nearly a thousand years later, the impact of that battle is still felt.

The build-up

When Edward the Confessor, the Anglo-Saxon King of England, died in 1066, he left no clear heir to his throne. Three contenders for the crown emerged: Harold Godwinson, Earl of Essex; Harald Hardrada, King of Norway; and William, Duke of Normandy in France. When Harold Godwinson was named king, he expected some opposition. Predicting an invasion from France, he gathered his troops in the south of England, poised for the attack. News soon arrived, however, that Harald Hardrada and his Viking army were on their way to the north of England. The troops quickly relocated and took the Vikings by surprise. Harold's quick response meant that the Vikings were defeated at the Battle of Stamford Bridge, near York, where Harald Hardrada was killed.

As Harold Godwinson's army was recovering from the battle, news arrived that William and his troops had arrived in the south of England. It was as Harold had originally expected – but his army was no longer ready. Nevertheless, the troops hurried south to meet the Norman invaders.

The battle

William's huge fleet of around 700 ships had landed at Pevensey Bay, in Sussex, on 29 September 1066. They raided the local areas and set about readying themselves for battle. Harold and his forces were back in London only by 12 October. Harold gathered what extra support he could and then proceeded towards Hastings.

When the two sides met at Senlac Hill on 14 October, Harold's troops were still exhausted. They were unmotivated and poorly paid. William's troops, however, were well prepared.

Some debate surrounds the size of the two armies. It is thought that each side had between 5,000 and 7,000 men, although both may have been bigger. William's troops were thought to have not only included Normans but also men from Brittany, Aquitaine and Maine, whom he had persuaded to support his invasion – in large part because he had received the Pope's blessing for his actions.

The forces steadied themselves for the confrontation. Harold's troops gathered at the top of the hill, forming a wall of shields. The Normans on foot fired arrows, while others on horseback charged up the hill. A rumour soon spread amongst the Normans that William had been killed, causing unrest and panic. William, however, is said to have removed his helmet and declared, 'Look at me! I'm alive and with the aid of God I shall gain the victory!' This rejuvenated his troops' spirits immediately.

It is also believed that the battle took a significant turn when the Normans pretended to run away. When they were chased, they turned and attacked – forcing Harold's army to lose the advantage of controlling the hill.

Harold's troops put up a brave fight against the Normans. The king, however, was killed in the battle, alongside his two brothers. Legend has it that he was wounded by an arrow in the eye and then was charged down. In total, around 10,000 men died in the battle.

Our understanding of the fighting, now commonly known as the Battle of Hastings, is much clearer than other events of the time. The Bayeux Tapestry, made soon afterwards, depicts the story of events from 1064 to the end of the battle. The chronicles and memoirs of the well-connected William of Poitiers, a Norman soldier, also provide us with vital information. However, it is important to remember that all of these surviving records were created from a Norman viewpoint. As is often the case, history was written by the victors.

The repercussions

Following the bloody battle, on Christmas Day 1066 William was crowned King of England at Westminster Abbey. The coronation marked the end of Anglo-Saxon rule and heralded a new period in British history. Gradually, the Norman influence transformed England and its language, law, customs and even architecture.

William had Harold buried next to the battlefield with a headstone reading 'Here lies Harold, King of the English', and built Battle Abbey on the site as an act of respectful penance. However, years later, Normans forgot William's humbleness. They destroyed the headstone and dug up Harold. His body now rests at Waltham Abbey, near London.

William is now often referred to as William the Conqueror – a just title.

 FILL IN THE GAP

Read the sentences and choose the correct word or words to fill the gap.

On the morning of 14 October 1066, two armies prepared to fight for the
_____ of England.

William's huge fleet of around _____ had landed at Pevensey Bay, in Sussex, on 29 September 1066.

The troops quickly _____ and took the Vikings by surprise.

The _____, made soon afterwards, depicts the story of events from 1064 to the end of the battle.

Harold's troops gathered at the top of the hill, forming a _____.

A rumour soon spread amongst the _____ that William had been killed, causing unrest and panic.

It is thought that each side had between 5,000 and 7,000 men, although both may have been
_____.

Following the bloody battle, on Christmas Day 1066 William was crowned King of England at
_____.

William is now often referred to as William the _____ – a just title.

When _____ was named king, he expected some opposition.

When the two sides met at Senlac Hill on _____, Harold's troops were still exhausted.

They were unmotivated and _____. William's troops, however, were well prepared.

Harold's quick response meant that the Vikings were defeated at the _____, near York, where Harald Hardrada was killed.

The _____ and memoirs of the well-connected William of Poitiers, a Norman soldier, also provide us with vital information.

The Normans on foot _____, while others on horseback charged up the hill.

MATCHING

Draw a line with a ruler to match the information.

the battle began	fired arrows
Harold's troops	alongside his two brothers
the king was killed	in the morning
the Normans on foot	put up a brave fight

predicted an invasion from France	at Westminster Abbey
legend says Harold died by	unmotivated and poorly paid
William was crowned King of England	an arrow lodged in his eye
Harold's troops were	Harold Godwinson

William's huge fleet	Battle of Stamford Bridge
supported invasion of England	Battle of Hastings began
Vikings were defeated	700 ships
14 October 1066	men from Brittany, Aquitaine and Maine

depicts the Battle of Hastings	left no heir to his throne
the two sides met at	famous and bloody battle
Edward the Confessor	the Bayeux Tapestry
the Battle of Hastings	Senlac Hill

Harald Hardrada	landed in Pevensey Bay, Sussex
Duke of Normandy	had a Viking army
killed at the Battle of Stamford Bridge	William
William's fleet	Harald Hardrada

◎ MULTIPLE CHOICE

Circle the correct answer for each of the following questions.

When did William's fleet land in Pevensey Bay, Sussex?

| 29 September | 19 September | 14 October | 12 October |

When did the Battle of Hastings begin?

| 10 October | 29 September | 14 October | 12 October |

Which King of England died in 1066?

| Duke of Normandy | Harald Hardrada | Edward the Confessor | William of Poitiers |

When did the Battle of Hastings begin?

| afternoon | evening | morning | night |

Who was killed by an arrow to the eye?

| Duke of Normandy | Harold Godwinson | Edward the Confessor | William of Poitiers |

Which people supported Harald Hardrada?

| Normans | Anglo-Saxons | Vikings | French |

How many ships were in William's fleet?

| 400 | around 500 | 600 | around 700 |

How many men died at the Battle of Hastings?

| 9,000 | around 10,000 | 11,000 | around 12,000 |

Whose chronicles tell us about the Battle of Hastings?

| Duke of Normandy | Harald Hardrada | Edward the Confessor | William of Poitiers |

Where did the two sides in the Battle of Hastings first meet?

| Senlac Hill | Stamford Bridge | York | Kent |

👎 TRUE OR FALSE

Read the sentences. Put a tick in the correct box to show which sentences are *true* and which are *false*.

Edward the Confessor was King of France.   True ☐ False ☐

William's huge fleet of ships landed at Stamford Bridge.   True ☐ False ☐

The Battle of Hastings began on 14 October 1066.   True ☐ False ☐

The Normans raided local areas near Pevensey.   True ☐ False ☐

Legend has it that Harold was wounded by an arrow in the knee.   True ☐ False ☐

The Normans charged on horseback.   True ☐ False ☐

Harald Hardrada was defeated by Harold Godwinson.   True ☐ False ☐

Edward the Confessor left the throne to his son.   True ☐ False ☐

The Bayeux Tapestry tells the story of the Battle of Hastings.   True ☐ False ☐

Harold's body can be found at Westminster Abbey.   True ☐ False ☐

The Duke of Normandy was William the Conqueror.   True ☐ False ☐

William was crowned king on Christmas Day.   True ☐ False ☐

William of Poitiers' memoirs tell the story of the Battle of Hastings.   True ☐ False ☐

2,000 men died in the Battle of Hastings.   True ☐ False ☐

William's army included men from Maine and Brittany.   True ☐ False ☐

2 BARACK OBAMA

On 4 November 2008, Barack Obama was elected the 44th president of the United States after securing more votes than any other presidential candidate in the history of the country. With his election, he became the first African American president of the country and went on to lead it through a period of turmoil and anxiety.

Obama was born in Hawaii on 4 August 1961. His mother, Stanley Ann Dunham (known as Ann) was from Kansas, in the United States. His father, Barack Obama Senior, was from Kenya, in Africa. The young Obama was raised with the support of his grandparents. His grandfather, who had a military background, and his grandmother, who worked her way up from secretary to manager positions in a bank, were hugely influential in his upbringing. Their key values and morals were later said to influence his presidency and his drive to ensure that every child, regardless of background, was given the same chances and opportunities without prejudice.

With the help of loans and scholarships, Obama worked his way through college before later moving to Chicago. With a church union, he helped to rebuild a number of communities that had been devastated by the closure of local steel plants. This life-changing experience helped to shape his belief in uniting people from different walks of life to create positive and meaningful change.

Obama later attended the prestigious Harvard Law School, in Cambridge Massachusetts, near Boston. There, at the age of 28, he became president of the *Harvard Law Review* – a student-run organisation that publishes legal journals.

After graduating, Barack began to teach constitutional law: the study, practice, interpretation and administration of laws based on the United States constitution. His career in politics began as he won seats in the Illinois State Senate and the United States Senate (part of the United States Congress, which is a small group of elected people who help decide the laws of the country).

In 2008, Obama was formally announced as the Democratic nominee for president of the United States. No other African American had ever received this honour. He fought a campaign against the Republican nominee, John McCain of Arizona state. A record number of voters took part in the election, and Obama eventually secured his victory on 4 November 2008.

An estimated two million people attended the formal ceremony to begin his presidency in Washington – thought to be the biggest ever audience for such an event.

Obama hoped that his election to the presidency would send a positive message to black students. He said: 'The fact that I've been elected shows

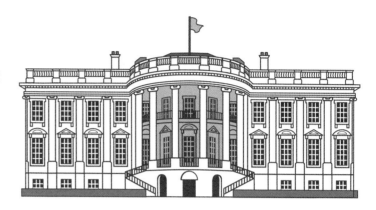

a lot of progress. It's encouraging – but it's important that stories like mine aren't used to say that everything is OK for blacks. You have to remember that, for every one of me, there are hundreds or thousands of black students with at least equal talent who don't get a chance.'

Obama took up what is arguably the world's most important job at an extremely problematic time in America, but immediately made his priorities clear.

In only his first few days, Obama directed the US military to begin withdrawing troops from Iraq. He ordered the closing of the Guantanamo Bay detention camp, which is a controversial US prison that poses a threat to human rights – although Congress blocked this order. He also gave financial aid to international family planning organisations, made legal changes to assist claims for equal pay for women and authorised a programme for children's health insurance.

Throughout his time in the White House, Obama helped to revitalise the economy of the country, reform the healthcare system and withdraw troops from war. He became an iconic and inspirational figure around the globe, and involved himself in the politics not only of the United States of America but also of the world. In 2009, Obama was awarded a prestigious Nobel Peace Prize for his efforts to strengthen international diplomacy and cooperation between people.

Barack Obama was succeeded as president of the United States by Donald Trump in 2016. Since leaving office, he and his wife Michelle, whom he met at a Chicago law firm, have continued to campaign for causes close to their heart, supporting and inspiring others. Michelle Obama has become an inspirational figure and role model for people across the world. She authored a book, *Becoming*, which discusses her life both inside and outside of the White House. The book quickly became a best seller.

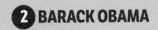

✏️ FILL IN THE GAP

Read the sentences and choose the correct word or words to fill the gap.

This life-changing experience helped to shape his belief in _____ people from different walks of life to create positive and meaningful change.

In 2009, Obama was awarded a prestigious _____ for his efforts to strengthen international diplomacy and cooperation between people.

His mother, Stanley Ann _____ (known as Ann) was from Kansas, in the United States.

Michelle Obama has become an _____ and role model for people across the world.

An estimated _____ people attended the formal ceremony to begin his presidency in Washington – thought to be the biggest ever audience for such an event.

Barack Obama was succeeded as President of the United States by _____ in 2016.

Since leaving office, he and his wife _____, whom he met at a Chicago law firm, have continued to campaign for causes close to their heart, supporting and inspiring others.

With the help of loans and _____, Obama worked his way through college before later moving to Chicago.

Throughout his time in the White House, Obama helped to revitalise the _____ of the country, reform the healthcare system and withdraw troops from war.

Their key values and morals were later said to influence his presidency and his drive to ensure that every child, regardless of _____, was given the same chances and opportunities without prejudice.

In 2008, Obama was formally announced as the _____ nominee for President of the United States.

With his election, he became the first _____ president of the country and went on to lead it through a period of turmoil and anxiety.

Obama took up what is arguably the world's most important job at an extremely problematic time in _____, but immediately made his priorities clear.

After graduating, Barack began to teach constitutional law: the study, practice, interpretation and administration of laws based on the _____ constitution.

Obama later attended the prestigious _____, in Cambridge Massachusetts, near Boston.

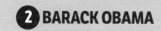

 **MATCHING**

Draw a line with a ruler to match the information.

Kansas	Barack Obama Senior
Kenya	Harvard
Arizona	Stanley Ann Dunham
Massachusetts	John McCain

Donald Trump	military background
Barack Obama	succeeded Obama as president
Michelle Obama	wrote *Becoming* book
grandfather	Nobel Peace Prize winner

presidential inauguration in	African-American president
studied law at	Chicago
worked with churches in	Harvard Law School
became the first	Washington

gave financial aid to	to assist claims for equal pay for women
authorised	begin withdrawing from Iraq
directed the military to	international family planning organisations
made legal changes	programme for children's health insurance

Obama elected	1961
Trump succeeded Obama as president	2009
Obama born	2008
Obama awarded Nobel Peace Prize	2016

⊙ MULTIPLE CHOICE

Circle the correct answer for each of the following questions.

Barack Obama was elected the _____ president of the United States.

| 43rd | 44th | 45th | 46th |

Who succeeded Obama as president?

| Bill Clinton | Michelle Obama | Donald Trump | John McCain |

What was Obama awarded in 2009 for his diplomatic work?

| the presidential Medal | a knighthood | a second presidency | a Nobel Peace Prize |

In 2008, which other presidential candidate was Obama competing against?

| John McCain | Stanley Ann Dunham | Donald Trump | Hillary Clinton |

Which prestigious law school did Obama attend?

| Harvard Law School | Cambridge Law School | Chicago Law School | Illinois Law School |

What helped Obama work his way through college?

| his mum | his friends | charities | loans and scholarships |

Where was Obama's father born?

| Hawaii | Kansas | Kenya | Washington |

What is the title of Michelle Obama's bestselling book?

| *Becoming* | *Become* | *Became* | *Harvard Law Review* |

How old was Obama when he became president of the Harvard Law Review?

| 25 | 26 | 27 | 28 |

What did Obama teach after graduating from law school?

| Politics | Science | History | Law |

👎 TRUE OR FALSE

Read the sentences. Put a tick in the correct box to show which sentences are *true* and which are *false*.

Harvard Law School is in Chicago.   True ☐ False ☐

Obama became president with more votes than ever before.   True ☐ False ☐

His grandfather had a military background.   True ☐ False ☐

A life-changing experience helped shape Barack's beliefs.   True ☐ False ☐

Three million people attended the formal ceremony in which Obama
became president.   True ☐ False ☐

Michelle Obama wrote a book called *Becoming*.   True ☐ False ☐

Barack Obama took over as president from Donald Trump.   True ☐ False ☐

The healthcare system was reformed under Obama.   True ☐ False ☐

America had lots of problems when Obama became president.   True ☐ False ☐

His Nobel Peace Prize was awarded for revitalising the economy of
the country.   True ☐ False ☐

Before he was president, Obama worked with local churches to rebuild
communities.   True ☐ False ☐

Obama was born in Alaska on 4 August 1961.   True ☐ False ☐

His grandmother worked her way from secretary to manager in a bank.   True ☐ False ☐

Obama's mother was born in Kenya.   True ☐ False ☐

Obama's father was called Stanley Ann Dunham.   True ☐ False ☐

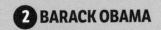 FIND AND COPY

These questions are about *Barack Obama*.

Look at paragraph one. Find and copy a word that suggests there was a great deal of uncertainty in America when Obama became president.

_____

Look at the second paragraph. Find and copy a phrase that suggests that Obama's grandparents were very important in his upbringing.

_____

Look at paragraph four. Find and copy a word that suggests that Barack studied at Harvard Law School.

_____

Look at paragraph three. Find and copy a word that suggests communities were affected badly by the closure of steel plants.

_____

Look at the paragraph beginning 'Throughout his time...'. Find and copy a word that suggests that Obama helped to change the healthcare system.

_____

Look at the final paragraph. Find and copy a word that suggests that Donald Trump became the new president after Barack Obama.

_____

Look at paragraph three. Find and copy a phrase that describes the impact that Obama's work with the church union had on him.

_____

Look at the paragraph beginning 'Obama took up...'. Find and copy a word that suggests that the situation in America was not simple or straightforward.

_____

✐ UNDERLINE OR HIGHLIGHT

Read the paragraphs below and then follow the instructions.

> Obama took up what is arguably the world's most important job at an extremely problematic time in America, but immediately made his priorities clear.
>
> In only his first few days, Obama directed the US military to begin withdrawing troops from Iraq. He ordered the closing of the Guantanamo Bay detention camp, which is a controversial US prison that poses a threat to human rights – although Congress blocked this order. He also gave financial aid to international family planning organisations, made legal changes to assist claims for equal pay for women and authorised a programme for children's health insurance.
>
> Throughout his time in the White House, Obama helped to revitalise the economy of the country, reform the healthcare system and withdraw troops from war. He became an iconic and inspirational figure around the globe, and involved himself in the politics not only of the United States of America but also of the world. In 2009, Obama was awarded a prestigious Nobel Peace Prize for his efforts to strengthen international diplomacy and cooperation between people.

Underline or highlight a word that means that there is evidence to support this point of view.

Underline or highlight a word that means to give something new life and energy.

Underline or highlight a word that means stopped or prevented.

Underline or highlight a word that means across or between different countries.

Underline or highlight a word that means the process of working together.

Underline or highlight a word that means to make someone feel they can achieve their dreams.

3 DINOSAURS

Dinosaurs became extinct tens of millions of years ago. Today, however, we're still fascinated by these staggering creatures – perhaps because understanding them and their extinction gives us a peek at the history of life on Earth.

Let's take a closer look at some of the world's favourite dinosaurs and what we've been able to discover about them.

Tyrannosaurus Rex

Lived: Late Cretaceous period, 68–66 million years ago

Undoubtedly, the Tyrannosaurus Rex is the most iconic dinosaur to have lived. This fearsome carnivore had 60 sharp, pointed teeth, each measuring up to 20 cm in length – around the size of a banana! Its hugely powerful jaws were able to crush bone, and its ferocious bite was around three times more powerful than that of a lion. A Tyrannosaurus Rex could grow up to 12 metres long, and stood at around 6 metres tall. It could weigh a hefty 7,000 kilograms.

No one knows whether the Tyrannosaurus Rex hunted alone or as part of a pack, but no groups of Tyrannosaurus Rex skeletons have yet been discovered. Scientists do know, however, that these creatures could run at speeds of up to 20 kilometres per hour, and that they had a fantastic sense of smell – both of which characteristics helped them to hunt live prey.

Triceratops

Lived: Late Cretaceous period, 68–66 million years ago

The Triceratops's unusual appearance means that it too has become instantly recognisable. It possessed a gigantic skull, which could measure around 3 metres long. Experts think its three horns, one above each eye and one on its snout, were used to fend off attacks from other dinosaurs. Similarly, the bony frill around its neck may have helped to protect it.

The Triceratops was a herbivore: it ate only plants and therefore did not hunt. Although many similar horned dinosaurs are known to have lived and travelled in groups, it is believed that the Triceratops lived a much more solitary life. Like those of the Tyrannosaurus Rex, Triceratops remains and skeletons are often found individually rather than in groups.

Stegosaurus

Lived: Late Jurassic period, 155–145 million years ago

Another striking dinosaur was the herbivorous Stegosaurus. Despite not being a hunter, it had a powerful, spiked tail that was a fearsome weapon. This was used for protection from predators. The Stegosaurus was the largest of the plate-backed plant eaters and was initially thought to have walked on two legs. It is now widely believed that it walked on four legs, but scientists are still not certain about the purpose of the plates along its back.

Unlike the Triceratops, the Stegosaurus had a small head compared to its body size, and a brain that was similar in size to a plum. Its large body, however, could grow to 9 metres in length.

Diplodocus

Lived: Late Jurassic period, 155–145 million years ago

Another famous herbivore, the Diplodocus was a huge creature. Weighing up to 20,000 kilograms, it could be up to 26 metres in length. The Diplodocus's size must have deterred potential attackers, and it would have also used its large, heavy tail as a weapon. Its long neck could have been used to reach high and low food sources, and allow it to drink water. Its rows of teeth were arranged like a comb, and were used to eat leaves from a variety of trees and soft plants. Like a Stegosaurus, the Diplodocus had a tiny head, which housed an even smaller brain.

Brachiosaurus

Lived: Late Jurassic period, 155–140 million years ago.

A dinosaur even more gigantic, the Brachiosaurus is thought to have weighed up to 25,000 kilograms and measured up to 30 metres in length. It stood at a height of more than 12 metres, which helped it to feed on foliage found high above the ground. It is estimated that a Brachiosaurus consumed between 200 and 400 kilograms of plants every day.

Coelophysis

Lived: Late Triassic period, 225–190 million years ago

Compared to others, the Coelophysis was a small dinosaur. It could grow to around 2 metres in length and weighed just 27 kilograms. The Coelophysis walked on two legs and used its size and rapid speed to catch a variety of animals, including insects and reptiles. Its small, sharp teeth were used to grasp and kill its prey.

Coelophysis means 'hollow form' which describes its hollow limb bones. This feature, also common in other small dinosaurs, meant the Coelophysis had a light body, which helped when hunting.

FILL IN THE GAP

Read the sentences and choose the correct word or words to fill the gap.

Today, however, we're still _____ by these staggering creatures – perhaps because understanding them and their extinction gives us a peek at the history of life on Earth.

Another striking dinosaur was the herbivorous _____.

Experts think its three horns, one above each eye and one on its _____, were used to fend off attacks from other dinosaurs.

This feature, also common in other small dinosaurs, meant the _____ had a light body, which helped when hunting.

A dinosaur even more gigantic, the _____ is thought to have weighed up to 25,000 kilograms and measured up to 30 metres in length.

Despite not being a hunter, it had a powerful, _____ that was a fearsome weapon.

This fearsome carnivore had 60 sharp, pointed teeth, each measuring up to 20cm in length – around the size of a _____!

The Coelophysis walked on two legs and used its size and _____ speed to catch a variety of animals, including insects and reptiles.

A _____ could grow up to 12 metres long, and stood at around 6 metres tall.

Unlike the Triceratops, the Stegosaurus had a small head compared to its body size, and a _____ that was similar in size to a plum.

The Diplodocus's size must have deterred _____ attackers, and it would have also used its large, heavy tail as a weapon.

Its long _____ could have been used to reach high and low food sources, and allow it to drink water.

Although many similar horned dinosaurs are known to have lived and travelled in groups, it is believed that the _____ lived a much more solitary life.

Like those of the Tyrannosaurus Rex, Triceratops remains and _____ are often found individually rather than in groups.

It possessed a _____, which could measure around 3 metres long.

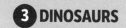

MATCHING

Draw a line with a ruler to match the information.

Tyrannosaurus Rex	teeth arranged like a comb
Stegosaurus	powerful, spiked tail
Triceratops	teeth the size of bananas
Diplodocus	3 metre skulls

Late Jurassic	Triceratops
Late Cretaceous	Coelophysis
Late Triassic	Tyrannosaurus Rex
Late Cretaceous	Stegosaurus

Stegosaurus	68-66 million years ago
Brachiosaurus	155–145 million years ago
Tyrannosaurus Rex	155–140 million years ago
Coelophysis	225–190 million years ago

consumed 200–400 kilograms of plants every day	Coelophysis
ate only plants	Triceratops
the largest of the plate-backed plant eaters	Brachiosaurus
ate insects and reptiles	Stegosaurus

lived and travelled in groups	the most iconic dinosaur
dinosaurs became extinct	brain the size of a plum
Stegosaurus	many horned dinosaurs
Tyrannosaurus Rex	tens of millions of years ago

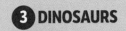

Label the description with the correct dinosaur.

the most iconic dinosaur that ever lived	
three horns	
fed on foliage high above the ground	
teeth like a comb	
brain similar size to plum	
name means 'hollow form'	

Label the description with the correct dinosaur.

consumed 200–400kg of plants	
used heavy tail as a weapon	
powerful, spiked tail	
frilled neck	
banana-sized teeth	
weighed just 27 kilograms	

Label the dinosaur with the correct time period, e.g. Late Triassic.

Stegosaurus	
Tyrannosaurus Rex	
Coelophysis	
Triceratops	
Diplodocus	
Brachiosaurus	

123 SEQUENCING

Look at *Dinosaurs*. Number the statements from 1 to 5 to show the order they occur in the text. Look at the first line of each paragraph to help you.

A dinosaur even more gigantic, the Brachiosaurus is thought to have weighed up to 25,000 kilograms and measured up to 30 metres in length.

Undoubtedly, the Tyrannosaurus Rex is the most iconic dinosaur to have lived.

No one knows whether the Tyrannosaurus Rex hunted alone or as part of a pack, but no groups of Tyrannosaurus Rex skeletons have yet been discovered.

Another famous herbivore, the Diplodocus was a huge creature.

The Triceratops's unusual appearance means that it too has become instantly recognisable.

Look at the 'Tyrannosaurus Rex' section in *Dinosaurs*. Number the statements from 1 to 5 to show the order they occur in the text.

It could weigh a hefty 7,000 kilograms.

This fearsome carnivore had 60 sharp, pointed teeth, each measuring up to 20 cm in length – around the size of a banana!

Undoubtedly, the Tyrannosaurus Rex is the most iconic dinosaur to have lived.

A Tyrannosaurus Rex could grow up to 12 metres long and stood at around 6 metres tall.

Its hugely powerful jaws were able to crush bone, and its ferocious bite was around three times more powerful than that of a lion.

Look at *Dinosaurs*. Number the statements from 1 to 5 to show the order they occur in the text.

Experts think its three horns, one above each eye and one on its snout, were used to fend off attacks from other dinosaurs.

Today, however, we're still fascinated by these staggering creatures – perhaps because understanding them and their extinction gives us a peek at the beginnings of life and death on Earth.

Scientists do know, however, that these creatures could run at speeds of up to 20 kilometres per hour and that they had a fantastic sense of smell – both of which characteristics helped them to hunt live prey.

It stood at a height of more than 12 metres, which helped it to feed on foliage found high above the ground.

It is now widely believed that it walked on four legs, but scientists are still not certain about the purpose of the plates along its back.

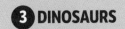 **FIND AND COPY**

These questions are about *Dinosaurs*.

Look at the 'Tyrannosaurus Rex' section. Find and copy a word that suggests other dinosaurs were scared of the Tyrannosaurus Rex.

_____

Look at 'Triceratops' section. Find and copy a word that suggests the Triceratops may have looked different to other dinosaurs.

_____

Look at the first paragraph of Dinosaurs. Find and copy a word that suggests humans are very interested in dinosaurs.

_____

Look at the first paragraph of Dinosaurs. Find and copy a word that suggests dinosaurs died out.

_____

Look at the 'Stegosaurus' section. Find and copy a word that suggests 'at first' or 'in the beginning'.

_____

Look at the 'Coelophysis' section. Find and copy a word that tells us that it was a quick moving animal.

_____

Look at the 'Diplodocus' section. Find and copy a word that suggests other dinosaurs might be discouraged or put off.

_____

Look at the 'Brachiosaurus' section. Find and copy a word that means plants and vegetation.

_____

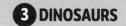

 ✏ UNDERLINE OR HIGHLIGHT

Read the paragraphs below and then follow the instructions.

Triceratops

Lived: Late Cretaceous period, 68–66 million years ago

The Triceratops's unusual appearance means that it too has become instantly recognisable. It possessed a gigantic skull, which could measure around 3 metres long. Experts think its three horns, one above each eye and one on its snout, were used to fend off attacks from other dinosaurs. Similarly, the bony frill around its neck may have helped to protect it.

The Triceratops was a herbivore: it ate only plants and therefore did not hunt. Although many similar horned dinosaurs are known to have lived and travelled in groups, it is believed that the Triceratops lived a much more solitary life. Like those of the Tyrannosaurus Rex, Triceratops remains and skeletons are often found individually rather than in groups.

Underline or highlight a word that means to live alone.

Underline or highlight a word that means to feed on plants.

Underline or highlight a word that means extremely large.

Underline or highlight a phrase that means to defend from an attack.

Underline or highlight a word that means out of the ordinary.

Underline or highlight a word that means people who are extremely knowledgeable about a subject.

4 CLIMATE CHANGE

Climate change: it's a term that everyone recognises, but few people fully understand it. Climate change and its effects are believed to be having a hugely negative effect on our planet. Scientists have warned that it may be too late to rectify the situation – but they are determined that everyone should try to understand how our world is changing, and know what they can do about it.

What exactly is climate change?

Earth's temperature is maintained by a layer of naturally occurring 'greenhouse gases'. These gases trap surface heat from the planet and prevent it from escaping into space. They are named because they behave like a greenhouse, helping to keep Earth warm and maintain its temperature. Experts state that, without these vital gases, the temperature on Earth would be around 30°C colder.

However, the concentration of gases that form this greenhouse effect is changing. Our planet and its inhabitants are producing and releasing other gases, and these gases result in more heat being trapped. As a result, the temperature of Earth is increasing, and more extreme weather is being created. This process is commonly known as 'global warming'.

What is causing climate change?

Carbon dioxide is believed to be the most significant contributor to climate change. About two thirds of greenhouse-gas pollution come from carbon dioxide, which is released when fossil fuels such as coal, gas and oil are burned. These forms of fuel are used as energy supplies across the world. Many simple everyday actions such as watching television and using lights also create carbon dioxide.

Deforestation is a connected contributing factor to climate change. Forests – including rainforests – absorb huge amounts of carbon dioxide from the air before releasing oxygen. As humans destroy more forest areas for their wood or to create farming or building land, there are fewer trees to remove carbon dioxide. The carbon dioxide is instead released into the atmosphere.

What has happened so far?

Over the last century, Earth's temperature is said to have increased by 1°C. Although this may not sound significant, even the smallest rise can have a serious effect. The polar ice caps have already begun to melt. A change in climate can lead to more unpredictable and extreme weather. It can result in wetter weather too, which some animals (including humans) may not be able to adapt to – so they may not be able to survive.

Significant shifts in temperature are nothing new on Earth. After all, our planet has seen tropical climates and ice ages come and go during its billions of years of existence. The concern now, however, is that temperatures are rising more rapidly than they have previously – and that, as a society, we are releasing more harmful gases into the Earth's atmosphere than ever before. Some climate scientists predict that Earth's temperature could increase by anything from 1.4°C to 5.8°C over the next 100 years.

What effects could climate change have?

The effects of climate change have already been seen in the wild, in various environments and among a variety of species. The habitat of polar creatures is at risk due to the rising temperatures around the North and South Poles. Polar bears rely on ice to raise their young and hunt, so the destruction of their icy habitat will have serious implications for their species.

As sea ice melts sea levels rise – and other creatures are affected by the changing conditions in different ways. Rising sea levels, for example, affect the ability of sea turtles to use beaches to lay their eggs. They could also change coastal habitats for many other animals and birds.

Climate change is affecting the human population too. Food production and farming has been disrupted by higher temperatures, increased rainfall, floods and even droughts. As sea levels rise, they will reduce island countries' areas considerably.

How can we prevent climate change?

Ultimately, the amount of harmful gases released from Earth needs to decrease significantly. Scientists are developing more ways to use renewable energy from the tides, the wind, the sun and Earth's heat. There are also, however, lots of small steps that everyone could take to help combat climate change. Turning off electrical items when they're not in use, walking or cycling instead of using a car and switching to energy-saving light bulbs are all ways to help protect our planet. Reducing food waste and recycling also make big differences.

Experts say it is essential for everyone to play their part in safeguarding the future of our planet.

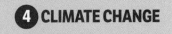

LABEL

Label the description with the correct fuel category: renewable energy or fossil fuel.

wind	
coal	
tidal	
gas	
sun/solar	
oil	

Label the description with the correct information.

who has warned it may be too late to rectify the situation	
name of the layer of naturally occurring gases	
the Earth becoming warmer is known as	
society is releasing more of these than before	
turning off may these help protect the planet	
climate change can lead to	

Label the description with the correct gas.

trees can absorb	
fossil fuels release	
trees release	
stops heat from escaping to space	
watching television and using lights creates	

123 SEQUENCING

Look at *Climate change*. Number the statements from 1 to 5 to show the order they occur in the text. Look at the first line of each paragraph to help you.

The effects of climate change have already been seen in the wild, in various environments and among a variety of species.

Earth's temperature is maintained by a layer of naturally occurring 'greenhouse gases'.

Deforestation is a connected contributing factor to climate change.

Ultimately, the amount of harmful gases released from Earth needs to decrease significantly.

However, the concentration of gases that form this greenhouse effect is changing.

Look at the 'How can we prevent climate change?' section in *Climate change*. Number the statements from 1 to 5 to show the order they occur in the text.

There are also, however, lots of small steps that everyone could take to help combat climate change.

Ultimately, the amount of harmful gases released from Earth needs to decrease significantly.

Reducing food waste and recycling also make big differences.

Scientists are developing more ways to use renewable energy from the tides, the wind, the sun and Earth's heat.

Turning off electrical items when they're not in use, walking or cycling instead of using a car, and switching to energy-saving light bulbs are all ways to help protect our planet.

Look at *Climate change*. Number the statements from 1 to 5 to show the order they occur in the text.

These gases trap surface heat from the planet and prevent them from escaping into space.

Many simple everyday actions such as watching television and using lights also create carbon dioxide.

This process is commonly known as 'global warming'.

Reducing food waste and recycling also make big differences.

Some climate scientists predict that Earth's temperature could increase by anything from 1.4°C to 5.8°C over the next 100 years.

◉ MULTIPLE CHOICE

Circle the correct answer for each of the following questions.

Greenhouse gases trap heat and prevent it from entering...

space	the environment	the atmosphere	the air

Climate change is a phrase that everyone...

believes	recognises	dislikes	is confused by

What is the commonly used term to describe the temperature on Earth increasing?

climate change	core warming	global warming	earth heating

Which gas is considered to be a significant contributor to climate change?

oxygen	water	nitrogen	carbon dioxide

What is the name given to coal, oil and gas?

renewable energy	safe fuels	green energy	fossil fuels

How many degrees has Earth's temperature increased by in the last century?

1°C	2°C	5°C	1.4°C

What is being destroyed that helps absorb huge amounts of carbon dioxide?

rainforests	the atmosphere	fossil fuels	sea ice

What is the name given to energy taken from tides, the wind, the sun and Earth's heat?

renewable energy	safe fuels	green energy	fossil fuels

What do polar bears rely on to hunt and raise their young?

seals	camouflage	ice	warm temperatures

Climate change can lead to...

predictable weather	normal weather	only dry weather	unpredictable weather

 **TRUE OR FALSE**

Read the sentences. Put a tick in the correct box to show which sentences are *true* and which are *false*.

Earth's temperature has risen over the last century. True ☐ False ☐

Scientists think it may be too late to stop climate change. True ☐ False ☐

Greenhouse gases help maintain Earth's temperature. True ☐ False ☐

Recycling adds to the climate change problem. True ☐ False ☐

Climate change is reducing sea levels around the world. True ☐ False ☐

Over the last century, Earth's temperature has increased by 5°C. True ☐ False ☐

Rainforests absorb carbon dioxide and give out oxygen. True ☐ False ☐

Humans are destroying more forest areas. True ☐ False ☐

Trees release carbon dioxide. True ☐ False ☐

The amount of harmful gases released from Earth needs to increase significantly. True ☐ False ☐

Cycling rather than using a car will help protect the planet. True ☐ False ☐

Rising sea levels is only likely to affect the animals of the Arctic. True ☐ False ☐

Earth has never seen tropical climates or ice ages before. True ☐ False ☐

Food production and farming has been affected by climate change. True ☐ False ☐

Droughts, floods, increased rainfall and high temperatures are caused by climate change. True ☐ False ☐

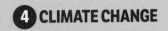

FIND AND COPY

These questions are about *Climate change*.

Look at the first paragraph. Find and copy a word that suggests that climate change tends to cause harm to our planet.

_____

Look at the second paragraph. Find and copy a word that suggests that the Earth's temperature is kept the same.

_____

Look at the 'What has happened so far?' section. Find and copy a word that suggests that we cannot know in advance what the weather will be like.

_____

Look at the paragraph beginning 'Carbon dioxide is believed…'. Find and copy a word that suggests carbon dioxide is the main reason why climate change is happening.

_____

Look at the paragraph beginning 'Deforestation'. Find and copy a word that suggests carbon dioxide is soaked up by trees in rainforests.

_____

Look at the 'What has happened so far?' section. Find and copy a word that suggests temperatures are rising at a great rate.

_____

Look at the 'What has happened so far?' section. Find and copy a word that suggests society is anxious about rising temperatures.

_____

Look at the 'How can we prevent climate change?' section. Find and copy a word that suggests an energy source is not used up or depleted when used.

_____

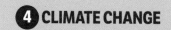UNDERLINE OR HIGHLIGHT

Read the paragraphs below and then follow the instructions.

> ## What effects could climate change have?
>
> The effects of climate change have already been seen in the wild, in various environments and among a variety of species. The habitat of polar creatures is at risk due to the rising temperatures around the North and South Poles. Polar bears rely on ice to raise their young and hunt, so the destruction of their icy habitat will have serious implications for their species.
>
> As sea ice melts sea levels rise – and other creatures are affected by the changing conditions in different ways. Rising sea levels, for example, affect the ability of sea turtles to use beaches to lay their eggs. They could also change coastal habitats for many other animals and birds.
>
> Climate change is affecting the human population too. Food production and farming has been disrupted by higher temperatures, increased rainfall, floods and even droughts. As sea levels rise, they will reduce island countries' areas considerably.

Underline or highlight a word that means types of animals.

Underline or highlight a phrase that means exposed to harm or danger.

Underline or highlight a word that means to get smaller.

Underline or highlight a word that means land that is close to the sea.

Underline or highlight a word that means a period of time with very little or no rainfall.

Underline or highlight a word that means to cause so much damage to something that it no longer exists.

The ancient Maya civilised what is now Mexico and Central America in the same way that the ancient Egyptians civilised Egypt. Their advances were extraordinary.

Who were the ancient Maya?

The ancient Mayan civilisation developed in Mesoamerica – an area made up of what is now known as Mexico and Central America – between 2000 BCE and 1500 CE. The Maya were extremely sophisticated. They were advanced in writing, art, science and architecture: they developed literature, sports, huge stone cities and a complex calendar.

Mayan society was divided into different levels, and the importance of an individual was represented by what they wore and the size of their headdress. Kings, who were at the top of society (and so had the biggest headdresses!), were believed to have god-like powers. Huge monuments were created to honour them.

The Maya created amazing cities of enormous proportions, lavishly decorated with images and text. They were characterised by impressive features such as temples, stepped pyramids, wide ball courts, observatories and palace complexes. Perhaps the most famous Mayan architecture is seen among the ruins of the city of Chichén Itzá. Its most recognisable structure is the stone-stepped Temple of Kukulkan, which has 365 steps – one for each day of the year. Each of the temple's four sides has 91 steps, and the top platform makes the 365th. It is now a leading tourist attraction in Mexico.

Although they shared beliefs, traditions and cultures, each city governed itself and had its own ruler.

What was life like for the ancient Maya?

The Mayan way of life may be unfamiliar in many ways, but it had an impact that still influences the modern world.

Mayan monuments and cities were developed over thousands of years. During this time, the Maya developed as farmers – creating methods still used today. They learned that burning areas of forest would create nutrient-rich ash, which turned soil into highly fertile land.

Farming was incredibly important for the Maya, who grew numerous crops such as maize, avocados, beans and squash. Most families grew their own crops and, if they had any leftovers, traded them at a market. The Maya's expertise at farming was also helped by their knowledge of astronomy. They understood the different seasons, and knew when was the best time to grow and harvest crops.

Families lived in small houses, in the cities or around them in nearby farmland. Men held jobs as farmers, warriors, hunters, builders and teachers, while women usually had roles at home. Children from noble families were educated in subjects such as maths, science, writing and astronomy. Those from poor backgrounds, however, were taught only their parents' jobs.

Children did not wear clothes until the age of five. At this point, ceremonies were held in which boys would receive loincloths and girls would receive skirts.

What did the ancient Maya believe?

Religion was hugely important for the Maya, and they had very strongly held beliefs. They believed in many different gods, who each represented a different aspect of life. Priests performed ceremonies in order to please the gods, and sacrifices were often made to them – they were usually animal sacrifices, but sometimes human! One of the most respected Mayan gods was Hun Ixim, the maize god. The Maya believed that this god controlled whether or not a crop would succeed or fail.

Another key belief of the Maya was the shape of the universe. It was believed that the universe was made up of a square, flat 'middle world', which rested on the back of a huge creature similar to a turtle. A giant tree stood in the centre of the middle world, with roots reaching into the underworld, known as Xibalba. The Maya believed that the evil and despised gods could be found here.

What happened to the Maya?

Many questions surround what actually brought ancient Maya rule to an end. Wars with other Mesoamerican people were common and bloody, and greatly reduced populations. However, one certainty is that, in 1517, Spanish conquistadors ('conquerors', who explored and seized land they found) began to conquer Maya land and crush their civilisation. They destroyed what they could and, as a result, very little Mayan literature remains.

Despite this, Mayan civilisation is not a thing of the past: millions of Maya still thrive. Around 7 million Maya still live in areas of Central America and southern Mexico. They have adapted to modern life, but maintain many of their values, traditions and heritage, including the languages they speak.

✏️ FILL IN THE GAP

Read the sentences and choose the correct word or words to fill the gap. Refer back to _Ancient Mayan civilisation_ to find the correct answer.

The ancient Mayan civilisation developed in _____ – an area made up of what is now known as Mexico and Central America – between 2000 BCE and 1500 CE.

Perhaps the most famous Mayan architecture is seen among the ruins of the city of _____.

Priests performed ceremonies in order to please the gods, and _____ were often made to them – they were usually animal sacrifices, but sometimes human!

🔗 MATCHING

Draw a line with a ruler to match the information.

famous city	•	•	Kukulkan
stone-stepped temple	•	•	Hun Ixim
respected god	•	•	Mexico and Central America
Mesoamerica	•	•	Chichén Itzá

✏️ LABEL

Label the description with the correct information.

the maize god	
a leading tourist attraction in Mexico	
four Mayan crops	
men's jobs in Mayan civilisation	
women's jobs in Mayan civilisation	
year in which Spanish conquistadors began to conquer Maya land	

✔️ TRUE OR FALSE

Read the sentences. Put a tick in the correct box to show which sentences are _true_ and which are _false_.

Kings were at the top of Mayan society.	True ☐	False ☐
The Mayans had a maize god.	True ☐	False ☐
The Mayan civilisation began in Europe.	True ☐	False ☐
The ancient Mayan civilisation developed between 2000 CE and 1500 BCE.	True ☐	False ☐
High monuments honoured the average worker.	True ☐	False ☐

◎ MULTIPLE CHOICE

Circle the correct answer to the following question.

How many steps does the Temple of Kukulkan have?

| 654 | 354 | 345 | 365 |

123 SEQUENCING

Look at *Ancient Mayan civilisation*. Number the statements from 1 to 4 to show the order they occur in the text.

The ancient Maya civilisation developed in Mesoamerica – an area made up of what is now known as Mexico and Central America – between 2000 BCE and 1500 CE.	
It is now a leading tourist attraction in Mexico.	
Although they shared beliefs, traditions and cultures, each city governed itself and had its own ruler.	
Kings, who were at the top of society (and so had the biggest headdresses!), were believed to have god-like powers.	

🔍 FIND AND COPY

These questions are about *Ancient Mayan civilisation*.

Look at the final paragraph. Find and copy a word that suggest the Mayan customs passed from generation to generation.

_____

Look at 'What happened to the Maya?' section. Find and copy a word that suggests that the Spanish tried to take control of the Mayan civilisation.

_____

🖊 UNDERLINE OR HIGHLIGHT

Read the paragraph below and then follow the instructions.

> The Maya were extremely sophisticated. They were advanced in writing, art, science and architecture: they developed literature, sports, huge stone cities and a complex calendar.

Underline or highlight a word that means the planning and construction of buildings.

Underline or highlight a word that means a record of the days, weeks and months.

6 PLANT ADAPTATIONS

Just like animals, plants need to be suited to their environments. They battle for water, air, light and nutrients, and to increase their ability to reproduce. They battle with each other, animals and their surroundings – and some of these surroundings make plants' jobs very difficult!

Despite that, every habitat on Earth is home to some plant life. Over millions of years, plants have grown to make the most of these habitats: the well-suited plants thrived and produced seedlings, and the badly suited ones died out.

The variety of their environments means that plants have had to develop some clever methods of survival.

Defeating drought

Desert plants such as cacti have fleshy stems with thick, waxy skins, which can store a lot of water. They have leaves with small surface areas, which reduces the risk of them drying up. Cactis' leaves are actually their spines! Desert plants grow far apart so their deep, wide root systems can absorb more of the little moisture they find under the dunes.

Flourishing in floods

In the rainforest, plants have the opposite problem: they have to cope with extreme rainfall. The leaves of rainforest trees have adapted to be thick and waxy, which means that heavy downpours are less likely to damage them. They also have pointed tips that act a little like spouts, draining water from their surfaces quickly. Soil beds in the rainforest are shallow – so, although trees' roots have no trouble finding moisture, they don't provide much support. Many tall rainforest trees have 'prop' roots that grow above the ground and act as wide, heavy bases.

Surviving the snow

Plant life in the coldest parts of Earth is sparse, but it does still grow. These environments share one feature with rainforests: only shallow root systems are possible. In polar regions, this is because only a little soil thaws each year, while the ground underneath it is permanently frozen. Plants grow tightly together, which provides the inner ones with some shelter from the harsh weather around them. They also develop fine hairs covering their stems to keep them warm. Because there is such a short time warm enough for insects to pollinate them, polar plants' flowers are strikingly coloured.

Withstanding the wind

Plants in high mountains grow close to the ground as protection from the wind. They seed outwards, covering wider surface areas. As well as allowing them to absorb more sunlight, this means that they too need only shallow root systems – which are all that are possible on rocky ground. The plants that do grow taller have developed flexible stems that can bend without breaking.

Standing up to the seasons

Western European climates have warm, sun-filled summers and frosty winters, so plants there need to be versatile. Many trees' leaves are wide and relatively fine, allowing broad canopies to spread and soak up sunlight when it is available. However, when winter comes, these leaves would gather too much snow. This is why deciduous trees have adapted to lose their leaves before the frostiest season begins.

Trees that do not lose their leaves (coniferous trees) have leaves that are small, glossy and needle-like. They are less likely to hold snow, which can slide off them. However, heavy snowfall can cover branches. These have, therefore, grown to be both strong and flexible. The branches' flexibility means that, once a layer of snow becomes heavy enough, they bend under it. The snow slides off, and the branches spring back into position.

Plants that attack!

Perhaps most surprisingly of all, some plants have adapted ways to kill for survival.

In the rainforest, vines called 'stranglers' grow. Their seeds settle and sprout high above the ground, on trees and other tall plants. Although their leaves grow fairly slowly, their roots grow quickly downwards – often over great distances from the seedling's high branch. When the roots reach the base of their tree, they wrap themselves around it. Slowly, their roots kill the trees. This leaves the strangler with a strong, tall tower it uses to reach more sunlight through the rainforest's canopy.

Some plants have adapted to grow in nutrient-poor soil by developing an even more grisly survival technique: they get their nutrients by eating insects. Pitcher plants lure insects to them using bright colours and sweet nectar. When a fly lands on a pitcher plant, which is shaped like a tall vase, slippery cells on the pitcher's curved lip make it slip down into the plant's hollow centre. There, a pool of digestive juices dissolves its prey.

🖋 FILL IN THE GAP

Read the sentences and choose the correct word or words to fill the gap. Refer back to *Plant adaptations* to find the correct answer.

They battle with each other, animals and their surroundings – and some of these _____ make plants' jobs very difficult!

The leaves of _____ trees have adapted to be thick and waxy, which means that heavy downpours are less likely to damage them.

This is why _____ trees have adapted to lose their leaves before the frostiest season begins.

🔗 MATCHING

Draw a line with a ruler to match the information.

rainforest	ground is permanently frozen
desert plant	flexible stems
coldest parts of earth	extreme rainfall
windy mountains	cacti

🏷 LABEL

Label the description with the correct information.

shallow soil beds	
plants grow tightly together	
plants grow roots above ground to support themselves	
plants that can bend without breaking have	
strangler vines grow	
plants develop fine hairs covering their stems to	

✅ TRUE OR FALSE

Read the sentences. Put a tick in the correct box to show which sentences are *true* and which are *false*.

Plants cannot grow in nutrient-poor soil.	True ☐	False ☐
Strangler vines kill trees to reach sunlight.	True ☐	False ☐
Pitcher plants lure insects for food.	True ☐	False ☐
All trees lose their leaves in winter.	True ☐	False ☐
It's never warm in Western Europe.	True ☐	False ☐

◎ MULTIPLE CHOICE

Circle the correct answer to the following question.

In which environment would you find a plant with waxy skin that can store lots of water?

mountainous hillsides	Western Europe	desert	polar

(123) SEQUENCING

Look at _Plant adaptations_. Number the statements from 1 to 4 to show the order they occur in the text.

They seed outwards, covering wider surface areas.	
They battle for water, air, light and nutrients, and to increase their ability to reproduce.	
Some plants have adapted to grow in nutrient-poor soil by developing an even more grisly survival technique: they get their nutrients by eating insects.	
This is why deciduous trees have adapted to lose their leaves before the frostiest season begins.	

◉ FIND AND COPY

These questions are about _Plant adaptations_.

Look at the 'Standing up to the seasons' section. Find and copy a word that describes trees that do not lose their leaves in winter.

_____

Look at the 'Surviving the snow' section. Find and copy a word that suggests that the ground is always frozen.

_____

◖ UNDERLINE OR HIGHLIGHT

Read the paragraph below and then follow the instructions.

> Trees that do not lose their leaves (coniferous trees) have leaves that are small, glossy and needle-like. They are less likely to hold snow, which can slide off them. However, heavy snowfall can cover branches.

Underline or highlight a word that means shiny.

Underline or highlight a word that means to move smoothly downwards.

7 HISTORY OF GAMING CONSOLES

The video games industry is worth billions of pounds, with gamers (both amateur and professional) to be found all across the world. Due to advances in technology, players can now enjoy high-calibre and affordable gaming in the comfort of their own homes. The industry has come a long way since the first video games console was created, though.

The 1960s

Video games began to become popular in the 1960s. At this time, however, they were played on computers so large that they took up entire tables – but with tiny screens. The first games console was planned by a German named Ralph Henry Baer. Although his design was basic, he is now known as 'the father of video games'.

The 1970s

In 1972, the Magnavox Odyssey became the first home video-game console to go on sale. Like modern games consoles, it allowed a user to insert different cartridges into the machine to play different games. It was an arcade game made by Atari though that really kick-started the industry: Pong, a game like table tennis. Seeing the potential, more electronics companies started tailoring their developments to home video gaming.

The 1980s

The video games industry continued to soar in the 1980s. In 1983, a Japanese developer named Nintendo released its Family Computer, which later became known as the Nintendo Entertainment System (NES). The console and its games featured higher-resolution graphics and details than had been seen previously. It soon became the highest-selling games console in the world, and one of its games' main characters – a plumber named Mario – quickly became a global celebrity.

A serious competitor to Nintendo emerged in the coming years as Sega – another Japanese company – entered the marketplace with its Master System console. Although its console did not enjoy the same kind of popularity as the NES, Sega grew to be a genuine contender to Nintendo in the games industry. At the end of the eighties, it released its Mega Drive, which instantly proved to be more popular than its predecessor.

The 1990s

Several smaller developers released their own home video games consoles as the decade began, but gaming fans took most note when Nintendo released its Super Famicom – now known as the Super NES (SNES). Soon afterwards, rival Sega released its own iconic game and character. Sonic the Hedgehog – a blue, sports-shoe-wearing hedgehog – became instantly popular, and remains as recognisable as Mario in the gaming industry.

In the coming years, the strong rivalry between Nintendo and Sega grew. Although, generally speaking, Nintendo reigned supreme in Japan, Sega was more popular in Europe. In the USA, however, they fought for their share of the market.

In the mid-nineties, Sony entered the market with its PlayStation console. Games were released on CDs, and Sony's 3D graphics were advanced. The PlayStation console became the first to sell over 100 million units worldwide, and dominated the years following its release. Nintendo released its Nintendo 64 console shortly afterwards. Despite iconic titles such as Super Mario 64 and Goldeneye, the console – which, unlike the PlayStation, still used cartridges for games – did not enjoy as much success. Towards the end of the nineties, Sega also released its own new console, the Dreamcast.

The 2000s

Early in the decade, three major consoles were released to the market: the Nintendo GameCube, the Sony PlayStation 2 and the Microsoft Xbox. All of them enjoyed success, but it was Sony's second PlayStation that flourished. It became the first console that could play DVDs and, even today, remains the best-selling home console of all time.

The noughties continued to see further advances in video game technology. Microsoft's Xbox 360 – which could be connected to four controllers wirelessly – was quickly followed by Sony's PlayStation 3. Around the same time, Nintendo released the Wii. With its unique controller, which was similar to a television remote, it used a sensor bar that required players to be active when playing games.

The 2010s

In response to Nintendo's motion-sensing technology, Microsoft launched its Kinnect console – which allowed users to play games in similar ways. This was followed by new consoles from all the major developers: Nintendo's Wii U, Sony's PlayStation 4 and Microsoft's Xbox One. The most popular of these consoles in terms of sales was the PlayStation 4, but millions of each of the other consoles were also sold worldwide.

The battle rages on for video-gaming supremacy, as the gaming giants push the boundaries of technology to be the first with the next major breakthrough – and start-up companies vie for a share of the market alongside them.

⊘ FILL IN THE GAP

Read the sentences and choose the correct word or words to fill the gap. Refer back to
History of gaming consoles **to find the correct answer.**

Like modern games consoles, it allowed a user to insert different _____ into the
machine to play different games.

In 1983, a Japanese developer named Nintendo released its _____, which later
became known as the Nintendo Entertainment System (NES).

With its unique controller, which was similar to a television remote, it used a
_____ that required players to be active when playing games.

⊕ MATCHING

Draw a line with a ruler to match the information.

Magnavox Odyssey •	• 1990s
Super Famicom •	• 1980s
Sega •	• 1970s
Kinnect •	• 2010s

⊘ LABEL

Label the description with the correct console or company name.

four wireless controllers	
Wii console	
Goldeneye	
Sonic the Hedgehog	
first home video console	
Mega Drive	

⊠ TRUE OR FALSE

Read the sentences. Put a tick in the correct box to show which sentences are *true* and which are *false*.

Nintendo is an American developer.	True ☐	False ☐
Ralph Henry Baer planned the first games console.	True ☐	False ☐
Xbox 360 was released in the eighties.	True ☐	False ☐
The Nintendo character Mario is an electrician.	True ☐	False ☐
The Wii controller is shaped like a remote control.	True ☐	False ☐

◎ MULTIPLE CHOICE

Circle the correct answer to the following question.

Which of the following was the first to be able to play DVDs?

PlayStation 2	Xbox	PlayStation 3	Nintendo 64

123 SEQUENCING

Look at *History of gaming consoles*. Number the statements from 1 to 4 to show the order they occur in the text.

NES	
Atari	
Master System	
Magnavox Odyssey	

🔍 FIND AND COPY

These questions are about *History of gaming consoles*.

Look at the 'The 1980s' section. Find and copy a word that suggests Sega became visible in the marketplace.

_____

Look at the 'The 1980s' section. Find and copy a word that suggests Mega Drive replaced the Master System which had come before it.

_____

❶ UNDERLINE OR HIGHLIGHT

Read the paragraph below and then follow the instructions.

It was an arcade game made by Atari though that really kick-started the industry: Pong, a game like table tennis. Seeing the potential, more electronics companies started tailoring their developments to home video gaming.

Underline or highlight a word that means to carefully consider and craft something based on specific requirements.

Underline or highlight a word that means to give impetus or start off.

ANSWERS

1. THE BATTLE OF HASTINGS

FILL IN THE GAP

1. throne
2. 700 ships
3. relocated
4. Bayeux Tapestry
5. wall of shields
6. Normans
7. bigger
8. Westminster Abbey
9. Conqueror
10. Harold Godwinson
11. 14 October
12. poorly paid
13. Battle of Stamford Bridge
14. chronicles
15. fired arrows

MATCHING

the battle began	in the morning
Harold's troops	put up a brave fight
the king was killed	alongside his two brothers
the Normans on foot	fired arrows
predicted an invasion from France	Harold Godwinson
legend says Harold died by	an arrow lodged in his eye
William was crowned King of England	at Westminster Abbey
Harold's troops were	unmotivated and poorly paid
William's huge fleet	700 ships
supported invasion of England	men from Brittany, Aquitaine and Maine
Vikings were defeated	Battle of Stamford Bridge
14 October 1066	Battle of Hastings began
depicts the Battle of Hastings	the Bayeux Tapestry
the two sides met at	Senlac Hill
Edward the Confessor	left no heir to his throne
the Battle of Hastings	famous and bloody battle
Harald Hardrada	had a Viking army
Duke of Normandy	William
killed at the Battle of Stamford Bridge	Harald Hardrada
William's fleet	landed in Pevensey Bay, Sussex

MULTIPLE CHOICE

1. 29 September
2. 14 October
3. Edward the Confessor
4. morning
5. Harold Godwinson
6. Vikings
7. around 700
8. around 10,000
9. William of Poitiers
10. Senlac Hill

TRUE OR FALSE

1. False
2. False
3. True
4. True
5. False
6. True
7. True
8. False
9. True
10. False
11. True
12. True
13. True
14. False
15. True

2. BARACK OBAMA

FILL IN THE GAP

1. uniting
2. Nobel Peace Prize
3. Dunham
4. inspirational figure
5. two million
6. Donald Trump
7. Michelle
8. scholarships
9. economy
10. background
11. Democratic
12. African American
13. America
14. United States
15. Harvard Law School

MATCHING

Kansas	Stanley Ann Dunham
Kenya	Barack Obama Senior
Arizona	John McCain
Massachusetts	Harvard
Donald Trump	succeeded Obama as president
Barack Obama	Nobel Peace Prize winner
Michelle Obama	wrote Becoming book
grandfather	military background
presidential inauguration in	Washington
studied law at	Harvard Law School
worked with churches in	Chicago
became the first	African-American president
gave financial aid to	international family planning organisations
authorised	programme for children's health insurance
directed the military to	begin withdrawing from Iraq
made legal changes	to assist claims for equal pay for women
Obama elected	2008
Trump succeeded Obama as president	2016
Obama born	1961
Obama awarded Nobel Peace Prize	2009

MULTIPLE CHOICE

1. 44th
2. Donald Trump
3. a Nobel Peace Prize
4. John McCain
5. Harvard Law School
6. loans and scholarships
7. Kenya
8. *Becoming*
9. 28
10. Law

TRUE OR FALSE

1. False
2. True
3. True
4. True
5. False
6. True
7. False
8. True
9. True
10. False
11. True
12. False
13. True
14. False
15. False

FIND AND COPY

1. turmoil
2. influential
3. attended
4. devastated
5. reform
6. succeeded
7. life-changing
8. problematic

UNDERLINE OR HIGHLIGHT

1. arguably
2. revitalise
3. blocked
4. international
5. cooperation
6. inspirational

3. DINOSAURS

FILL IN THE GAP

1. fascinated
2. Stegosaurus
3. snout
4. Coelophysis
5. Brachiosaurus
6. spiked tail
7. banana
8. rapid
9. Tyrannosaurus Rex
10. brain
11. potential
12. neck
13. Triceratops
14. skeletons
15. gigantic skull

MATCHING

Tyrannosaurus Rex	teeth the size of bananas
Stegosaurus	powerful, spiked tail
Triceratops	3 metre skulls
Diplodocus	teeth arranged like a comb
Late Jurassic	Stegosaurus
Late Cretaceous	Tyrannosaurus Rex
Late Triassic	Coelophysis
Late Cretaceous	Triceratops
Stegosaurus	155-145 million years ago
Brachiosaurus	155-140 million years ago
Tyrannosaurus Rex	68-66 million years ago
Coelophysis	225-190 million years ago
consumed 200-400 kilograms of plants every day	Brachiosaurus
ate only plants	Triceratops
the largest of the plate-backed plant eaters	Stegosaurus
ate insects and reptiles	Coelophysis
lived and travelled in groups	many horned dinosaurs
dinosaurs became extinct	tens of millions of years ago
Stegosaurus	brain the size of a plum
Tyrannosaurus Rex	the most iconic dinosaur

LABEL

1. Tyrannosaurus Rex
2. Triceratops
3. Brachiosaurus
4. Diplodocus
5. Stegosaurus
6. Coelophysis
7. Brachiosaurus
8. Stegosaurus
9. Stegosaurus
10. Triceratops
11. Tyrannosaurus Rex
12. Coelophysis
13. Late Jurassic
14. Late Cretaceous
15. Late Triassic
16. Late Cretaceous
17. Late Jurassic
18. Late Jurassic

SEQUENCING

5, 1, 2, 4, 3
5, 2, 1, 4, 3
3, 1, 2, 5, 4

FIND AND COPY

1. fearsome
2. unusual
3. fascinated
4. extinct
5. initially
6. rapid
7. deterred
8. foliage

UNDERLINE OR HIGHLIGHT

solitary
herbivore
gigantic
fend off
unusual
experts

4. CLIMATE CHANGE

LABEL

1. renewable (energy)
2. fossil fuel
3. renewable (energy)
4. fossil fuel
5. renewable (energy)
6. fossil fuel
7. scientists
8. greenhouse gases
9. global warming
10. harmful gases
11. electrical items
12. unpredictable and extreme weather
13. carbon dioxide
14. carbon dioxide
15. oxygen
16. greenhouse gases
17. carbon dioxide

SEQUENCING

4, 1, 3, 5, 2
3, 1, 5, 2, 4
1, 3, 2, 5, 4

MULTIPLE CHOICE

1. space
2. recognises
3. global warming
4. carbon dioxide
5. fossil fuels
6. 1°C
7. rainforests
8. renewable energy
9. ice
10. unpredictable weather

TRUE OR FALSE

1. True
2. True
3. True
4. False
5. False
6. False
7. True
8. True
9. False
10. False
11. True
12. False
13. False
14. True
15. True

FIND AND COPY

1. negative
2. maintained / maintain
3. unpredictable
4. (most) significant
5. absorb
6. rapidly
7. concern
8. renewable

UNDERLINE OR HIGHLIGHT

species
at risk
reduce
coastal
droughts
destruction

5. ANCIENT MAYAN CIVILISATION

FILL IN THE GAP

Mesoamerica
Chichén Itzá
sacrifices

MATCHING

famous city	Chichén Itzá
stone-stepped temple	Kukulkan
respected god	Hun Ixim
Mesoamerica	Mexico and Central America

LABEL

1. Hun Ixim
2. (Temple of) Kukulkan
3. maize, avocados, beans and squash
4. farmers, warriors, hunters, builders and teachers
5. roles at home
6. 1517

TRUE OR FALSE

1. True
2. True
3. False
4. False
5. False

MULTIPLE CHOICE

365

SEQUENCING

1, 3, 4, 2

FIND AND COPY

maintain
conquer

UNDERLINE OR HIGHLIGHT

architecture
calendar

6. PLANT ADAPTATIONS

FILL IN THE GAP

surroundings
rainforest
deciduous

MATCHING

rainforest	extreme rainfall
desert plant	cacti
coldest parts of earth	ground is permanently frozen
windy mountains	flexible stems

LABEL

1. rainforests
2. surviving the snow
3. rainforest trees
4. flexible stems
5. in the rainforest
6. survive the snow / keep them warm

TRUE OR FALSE

1. False
2. True
3. True
4. False
5. False

MULTIPLE CHOICE

desert

SEQUENCING

2, 1, 4, 3

FIND AND COPY

coniferous
permanently

UNDERLINE OR HIGHLIGHT

glossy
slide

7. HISTORY OF GAMING CONSOLES

FILL IN THE GAP

cartridges
Family Computer
sensor bar

MATCHING

Magnavox Odyssey	1970s
Super Famicom	1990s
Sega	1980s
Kinnect	2010s

LABEL

1. Microsoft's Xbox 360
2. Nintendo
3. Nintendo 64
4. Sega
5. Magnavox Odyssey
6. Sega

TRUE OR FALSE

1. False
2. True
3. False
4. False
5. True

MULTIPLE CHOICE

PlayStation 2

SEQUENCING

3, 2, 4, 1

FIND AND COPY

emerged / entered
predecessor

UNDERLINE OR HIGHLIGHT

tailoring
kick-start(ed)